The Dog on the
Tuckerbox

While I was writing this book, I had, for the shortest time, the privilege of knowing an old brown kelpie called Kate. She had the kindest and most loving nature and unbelievable courage; the same sorts of qualities I imagine were supreme in the dog who once sat on the tuckerbox.

C.F.

For Otto and his friends Basil, Bear, G.J., Harry, Lassie, Louis, Lola, Rosie, Roxy, Spud and the late Barry, faithful companions all.

P.G.

The Dog on the Tuckerbox

by Corinne Fenton & illustrated by Peter Gouldthorpe

Lady sat on the tuckerbox watching her master, Bill.
He packed up his billy and stamped out the campfire.
It was time to get moving.

'Off you go, girl,' Bill called to Lady. She knew what to do — round up the bullocks so Bill could yoke them.

Then the crack of Bill's greenhide whip rang out.
'Gee Diamond, gee Nobby!' The mighty bullocks pulled
with all their strength and the wagon began to roll.

The settlers who lived far out in the bush were
always pleased to see Bill. For long lonely months
he might be their only visitor.

He brought much needed supplies and
news from neighbouring homesteads.
And the children were always pleased
to see Lady.

Some nights Bill had the company of other teamsters or hawkers who travelled the same tracks.

In summer, stirred-up dust billowed from the wooden wheels and the hooves of the bullocks. Sometimes they travelled through the charred remains of a bushfire. It was on a day like this they came upon a stray bull.

The angry beast charged at Bill's team.
In a flash Lady was between the charging animal
and the bullocks. Still the bull thundered forward.

Barking bravely, Lady sprang at the bull's head.
The outraged bull flung Lady off as if she were a matchstick,
then turned and disappeared into the bush.

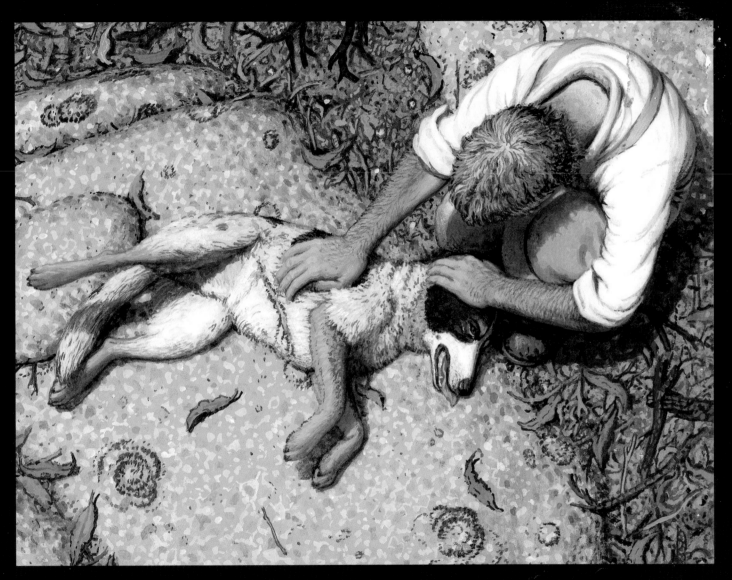

Lady lay still.

By the campfire Bill tended Lady's wounds.
'You saved us all today, my girl,' he said. 'That bull could have
spooked the whole team.'

Lady spent days lying under the wagon. On the fifth day, when she wagged her tail, Bill knew she was going to be all right.

Once again the crack of Bill's whip rang out through the bush.
In and out of the homesteads and all along the winding tracks,
Lady left her footprints.

Late one winter's afternoon, close to Gundagai, Bill stood at the
edge of a quagmire. In summer it had been nothing more than a narrow creek.
Bill whistled to Lady. 'Run ahead, girl, find us the best spot to cross.'
Minutes passed, finally Lady barked from the other side.

'Gee Diamond, gee Nobby,' Bill called.

Diamond edged forward — the rest of the team followed.

They were about half way across when Nobby broke the yoke and Bill heard the snap of a splintering axle.

Bill whistled long and low. Lady came running.

For a moment Bill leaned against the wagon.

Then he reached for his tuckerbox.

'Come on, girl,' he said.

Together they trudged across the quagmire.

For Bill there was no choice. He had to leave and get help.

'Stay on watch, Lady. You're a lass I can count on. My word you are.'

Maybe Bill lost his way somewhere
in the dark bush.
Or maybe he fell and lay injured.

The following day a passing
teamster released Bill's bullocks into
the bush. He noticed Lady sitting on
the tuckerbox, exactly as her master
had commanded.

Passing settlers and other bullockies tried to coax Lady to come with them, but she would not leave her place. They gave her what food they could spare. Still she waited, with a patience and faithfulness that could not be shaken. Bill never returned.

In 1932 a monument of a dog sitting on a tuckerbox
was erected five miles from Gundagai.

TUCKERBOX PIONEER MONUMENT GUNDAGAI

A tribute to our Pioneers

— UNVEILED BY —

The Rt. Hon. J. A. Lyons, P.C.
Prime Minister of the Commonwealth
28–11–1932

Earth's self upholds this monument,
To conquerors who won her when
Wooing was dangerous and now
Are gathered unto her again.

First published in 2008 by

black dog books

15 Gertrude Street
Fitzroy Vic 3065
Australia
61 + 3 + 9419 9406
61 + 3 + 9419 1214 (fax)
dog@bdb.com.au

Designed by Studio Pazzo Pty Ltd
Printed and Bound in China by Everbest Printing
Photographs courtesy of the State Library of Victoria

National Library of Australia
cataloguing-in-publication data:

Fenton, Corinne.

Dog on the Tuckerbox

For primary school children.

ISBN: 9-78-1742-03008-1 (hbk)

1. Dog on the Tucker Box (N.S.W.) — Juvenile literature.
2. Monuments — New South Wales — Gundagai — Juvenile literature
3. New South Wales — History — Juvenile literature

Dewey Number: 994.4

10 9 8 7 6 5 4 3 2 1   8 9 / 0

ACKNOWLEDGMENTS

I would like to thank the following people:

Dianne Cotterill and family for talking to me about Gundagai and the legend
Bruce Dennis and the Gundagai Museum for help and advice
Wendy Graham for always being honest
Rod Hutton, Secretary, Australian Bullock Drivers League Inc. who answered a thousand questions and gave invaluable help in every aspect of this book
Ron McKinnon, Australian Bullock Drivers League Inc. for assistance and contacts
Gabriel Gallery, Gundagai
Graham Young for advice on bullocks
Gundagai Library
Sue and Terry McDonald for help and guidance on all things 'dog'
Richard O'Leary, Glenmore Farm, for pointing me in the right direction.

And to my family who this time shared our home with a dog called Lady – much more manageable than an elephant!
to Peter Gouldthorpe for once again giving life to a beloved icon
to Maryann Ballantyne and everyone at Black Dog Books for believing in me again
and to all the dogs I observed, sat with, talked to and cuddled.

Corinne Fenton